HIV-MUSCLES

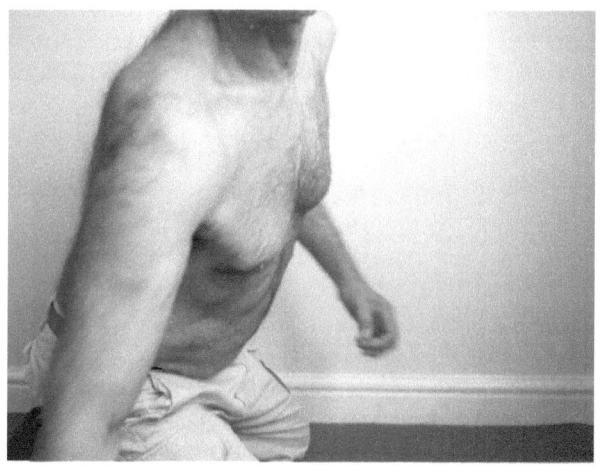

A book written
by

Irvin Beamish

to demonstrate a way to fight illness,
and win.

ISBN: 978-1-4834-1726-4 (sc)
ISBN: 978-1-4834-1727-1 (e)

Because of the dynamic nature of the Internet, any web addresses or links contained in this book may have changed since publication and may no longer be valid. The views expressed in this work are solely those of the author and do not necessarily reflect the views of the publisher, and the publisher hereby disclaims any responsibility for them.

Any people depicted in stock imagery provided by Thinkstock are models, and such images are being used for illustrative purposes only. Certain stock imagery © Thinkstock.

Lulu Publishing Services rev. date: 09/29/2014

Today Irvin is doing well. HIV Positive, as we are known, has now become HIV/AIDS. This is to make sure that we don't forget that HIV is the cause of aids. 15 June 2014 is the date today.

Now after nearly 28 years, I am still ok and not 'on my last legs' as was predicted all those years ago.

I believe that there is a way of fighting back and not being told that we have to be ill to prove the medics are right.

To be made to believe that one is afflicted with a deadly disease is devastating, but that is what happened to me in late 1986. Here is an accurate account of what happened over the years. Now I am doing ok, even getting a pension!

My name is Irvin Beamish, born in 1946.

Thinking that death would come to me sometime in the not-too-distant future, I did not really know what to expect. So I carried on as though things had not changed.

It's good to think that things have turned out better that I could have thought imaginable back in 1986. If HIV/AIDS is the devastating disease which we are constantly told, then it can't be that bad, can it?

I still don't know.

CHAPTER ONE

My HIV

In 1986 I attended a local hospital, and said that I wanted to take a test for HIV. I had been in sexual contact with someone who died a few weeks before, and I thought that as I felt perfectly well and healthy that there could be no possibility of me having anything that would make me ill. The publicity about HIV was scary and talk of death did not seem compatible with the way I was feeling. I believed that I could and would live for many years, and I seemed to have been correct. I took the test in 1986 but had been probably been exposed to HIV for some 2-3 years before that.

A sample of blood was taken from me, and after a week I returned to the hospital for the result. Instead of being given the result of the test, a nurse said that I needed to take another test. I asked why and was told that that was what was written on the information sheet, nothing else.

So I agreed to give another blood sample, and to come back in another week's time. This I did and was told that my results showed that I was HIV positive. A shocking and unexpected result, which I had not thought that this could have happened to me.

So 28 years later I look back and although I thought that I would not still be here at this time, I am glad that I am, and that I am living well, not at 'death's door' as I was predicted to have been in the 1980s. Today we still have no vaccine, but over the years expensive drugs and medicines have been developed which combat the HIV and can mean that people can be diagnosed HIV+ and not die quickly any more. In 1986 there were no drugs on offer as HIV had not been discovered until about 2 or 3 years before that time.

The word spread around the world in the 1980s, that aids was a new disease, and was caused by a virus which became to be known as HUMAN IMMUNODEFICIENCY virus.

So I must be doing something 'right'. At the time I was diagnosed I was expected to live for another five years, or perhaps less.

This information is perhaps useful for anyone who is thinking of getting tested for HIV. If the result is Positive, it will change your life, as it has done mine. I never believed that I could have such a deadly disease, and yet feel perfectly well at the same time.

The HIV virus has been around for a long time, no-one knows for certain how long. In 1976 I had swollen lymph nodes in my groin, and this was painless and did not cause me any discomfort.

I did not seek medical advice at the time, and did not feel unwell, and eventually things seemed to return to normal. Condoms were considered to be for contraception only, not for disease prevention purposes.

My job was physical and I could not find any reason to believe I was ill in any way. My energy levels did not seem to be any less than normal.

Today I'm still fit, and still not ready to die, as was predicted in 1986. No anti HIV medicines were available then, and so I carried on as 'normal'. I was told to return to the clinic every three months, where I was told my health would be checked.

After about two years my consultant announced that I was eligible for a 'new' drug called AZT, (zidovudine). As I did not feel unwell at the time, I declined, and said that I would prefer not to take AZT, but that someone else might benefit from it. The doctor was not pleased that I had done this;

Obviously to ignore a doctor's recommendation was something not normally done. I had a feeling that any medication was unnecessary at the time. As it turned out, and looking back I appear to have done the right thing. Some of my friends from the 1980s died and the reason given was Aids. They had been given AZT, and made to believe that this was their best bet for surviving. The AZT is a deadly toxic drug and a failed cancer drug from the 1960s. It was brought out of 'mothballs' to deal with HIV, as there was nothing else available at the time. Eventually other drugs began to appear and were being tried out. Today information can change quickly. The drugs available now are increasing in number by the year, and there is a long list of medications published now. These are classed by the way they deal with the HIV. Haart is an abbreviation for the treatment given at present. This stands for Highly Active Anti-Retroviral Therapy. After about 8 or 9 years of knowing I was HIV +, I was told by my medics at my clinic that I had done very well, and that I now needed to take medications. My cd4 count was low and I think I had a cold or flu or something. I was given AZT and Didanosine, a combination of two drugs.

Later on three drugs were considered to be the norm, and would have much greater and long-lasting effect than two.

This is known as Combination therapy, and is the present-day way of medicating patients with HIV.

There is a long list of medications available now, these fall into categories according to how they work.

On day, we are told that a cure for HIV may be available. Till then it is a matter of taking the medications as prescribed by the hospitals. Some have unpleasant side effects, some more tolerable than others. Over the years the treatments that have been developed have been successful, improving the health of many. The pills come in six types; according to which way they work in the body.

1. nucleotide or nucleoside reverse transcriptase inhibitors- NRTI class.
2. Non nucleoside reverse transcriptase inhibitors. NNRTI class.
3. Fixed dose NNRTI; - three drugs together in one pill.
4. Protease inhibitors.
5. Entry inhibitors,
6. Integrase inhibitors.

A total of approximately 25 varieties of drugs. Each comes in one of the above classes, and the consultant will prescribe usually three to be taken on a daily basis, sometimes with food, and sometimes without. The AZT I was prescribed made me feel weak and they said I was a bit anaemic, but I did not know that all this was caused by this medication. AZT is a substance to be avoided, in my opinion. I was relieved to find out that in 1988, had I agreed to take it, as a monotherapy, it might have caused me to be very ill, and that the reason for this was the 'virus' whereas the AZT was having the bad effect I would have been experiencing. Three people who I knew well were taking AZT back in the early 1990s, and died. Obviously they thought that their best way to live longer was to take more AZT, which was making them worse, not better. So my instincts were right: If I do not feel ill, why take strong medications?

As time went on I was changed to other types of drugs as they became available. After the AZT/ didanosine era came to an end I was given D4T and 3TC. D4T is not generally prescribed now, as it has been discovered to cause neuropathy in the feet. Something I had and still have, and this came on a few weeks after starting the D4T.

Neuropathy is a tingling feeling caused by nerve damage, and often it is known a Peripheral Neuropathy, as it can affect both the hands and feet. I find it gets worse when I get tired or generally feel as though I have become a bit 'run down'.

I am still able to walk ok and get about and take regular exercise.

Another treatment was also recommended by the hospital, and that in order to prevent a lung disease called Pneumo Cystis Carinni, I would need to take Pentamodine. This is a gas and is highly toxic, but at that time I thought that the doctors knew best, so I agreed. I was to wear a face mask and be connected to a gas cylinder and for about 20 minutes left to breathe this gas. The doctors and nurses were seemingly terrified of the gas and would make themselves scarce while I was breathing it into my lungs. This was done monthly, and soon I began to feel unwell, weak and lacking in energy. One day I went to my local surgery and the doctor thought that I had something wrong and sent me to the hospital for a chest X-ray.

On the x-ray there was a patch on my lungs which looked lighter than the rest. The medics said that it was PCP. As I had been to the clinic and had Pentamodine just a few days before, everyone looked a bit perplexed. They sent me to another hospital and started to give me heavy doses of Co-trimoxadole (septrin), to treat my condition. I stayed there for about a week, and on leaving felt much better. I think taking the Pentamodine made me feel ill, and after that I did not continue, or want to continue, with this treatment. I do not think it did me any good. There is a website showing a young boy sitting in an enclosed cabin and being given this gas. The cabin is to prevent the gas coming into contact with the staff, and the poor boy must be feeling dreadful I would imagine. I would not recommend anyone to use this treatment. Similarly AZT is a substance to be avoided, and I would not recommend that either.

I do not take substances which are toxic, such as heroin, cocaine or 'poppers', a substance often used by gays to increase blood flow, in the belief that this is a sexual stimulant. Alcohol is something I drink on only small amounts now, as I drive quite a lot.

Perhaps I have been lucky. I don't know. Some people seem to have a resistance to the HIV virus, perhaps this is nature's way of preserving the species.

A television programme transmitted a few years ago once explained how the great plague in Europe in the middle ages killed many thousands of people. Curiously there were those who came into contact with others with the disease, but remained uninfected. Research into this has indicated that a certain gene might have been present in some people, and caused the virus to be 'blocked' from entering their cells.

It was thought that I would have been dead back in the 1990s. Treatment was very basic at that time, and I was considered to be a sick person, and that I could possibly be kept alive for a year or two. I was told that I had been tested without my knowledge in early 1985, but as I had not asked for an HIV test at the time, the results of the 'secret' test were not disclosed to me. I had consulted a medic at that time who said that swollen glands, which I then had, happened to some people, and were considered of no consequence.

He said he would refer me to a large local hospital, if I wished to have further investigation into this condition. So I agreed to this. The hospital seemed to take a great interest in me, and I was given a biopsy, to examine my lymph glands in my neck. This meant I had to go and stay in the hospital for about 2 or 3 days. This biopsy, when I had the results, showed that there did not seem to be anything wrong, and that no treatment was necessary. So I left the hospital and felt quite healthy, not knowing that I had been given a 'secret' HIV test, and that was why the doctors examined me thoroughly before I left, I realised afterwards.

It was not until 1986 that I asked for an HIV test. The reason for this was that someone who I had had sex with in earlier years had died. They said that he had died of Aids, and this caused me to think that I might have something similar. As I felt perfectly well I thought that this could not be possible. How could someone who was in good health have the 'disease of the century?' When I took my test the results came back as HIV antibody positive, which came as a shock to me at that time.

The test looks for the antibodies for HIV, not the virus as such. If the antibodies are present then it assumes that the virus is or has been present in the human body.

My life changed but I still carried on working and I felt well and could not imagine being ill. Every three months I would go to the hospital and they would take blood samples and do tests. After 1996, which was around the time that the 'combination therapy' had started, I have taken D4T & 3TC, then tenofovir, Kivexa, Abacavir, Efavirenz, Nevirapine, Atripla (efavirenz, +ftc + tenofivir), (three drugs combined in one tablet).

This combination I could not tolerate, because the efavirenz had a strange effect on me mentally, and I felt as though I was not right for a few hours after taking it. Difficult to explain really.

These medications have been given to me over the years in the hope that I would 'stay alive'. What would have happened if I had not taken any it's hard to know. When I had thrush quite badly I was given V-Fend. This treats the thrush quite well and I take one tablet daily still as a preventative measure, and it seems to work well.

One day there may be a cure for HIV, at the moment there still is none. Treatments are improving as time goes on. When I began treatment in 1996 I was given combinations of two different drugs. This was because the Hospital I attended did not have a large range available at the time. It is now considered that HIV patients should be given three drugs in order to combat the effects of the virus.

Some countries are not fortunate enough to have treatments, or very little available. They are not affordable in poor countries. Now that 'generic' versions of the HIV drugs are becoming available, this may gradually change. Generics become available as the patents expire and allow other maufacturers to produce similar medicines at lesser cost.

CHAPTER TWO

A Short History of HIV

Gay men were the first to be diagnosed with 'mystery' illnesses, and there seemed to be little or no treatment for the people who were afflicted.

These illnesses included Karposi's sarcoma, a cancer which causes purple blotches on the skin.

Also PCP (pneumo cystis carinni), a disease of the lungs.

CMV, (CYTOMEGALOVIRUS) is another 'classic' aids illness. It affects the eyes, and can cause blindness.

In 1959 a sailor from Manchester, England, became ill and died from a mystery disease. He did not respond to any treatment available at that time. Looking back it looks as though this could have been an early case of aids, as the symptoms appeared to reflect those of aids patients today.

It has been said that HIV may have been transferred from chimpanzees to humans around the 1940s-1950s. Chimpanzees were hunted and there was a possibility that hunters were infected with their blood. The animal version is known as SIV, Simian Immunodeficiency Virus. Other monkeys that were hunted by the chimpanzees could have given the chimpanzees the virus, which then went on to infect humans. This is thought to have occurred in Africa and it was not until the early 1980s that the illness was recognised in America, notably in New York and San Francisco and Europe.

The word 'AIDS' was applied in the 1980s, this is an abbreviation of the words Acquired Immune Deficiency Syndrome. The SIV virus goes back in time possibly for many hundreds of years. It is known as a Retrovirus, and is similar to HIV.

Retrovirus means that it can take many years for the immune system to be damaged, and for symptoms to appear.

There are a number of theories of how the HIV virus spread rapidly in Africa and then round the world. Contaminated syringes used for medical purposes, and squalid conditions endured by natives in colonial times.

A recent development has been the apparent cure of a patient in Germany. He was given a bone marrow transplant for leukaemia, he also had HIV. After the treatment He appeared to have been cleared of HIV. The case came about not through research but by chance. No-one had ever thought of this before as a treatment, but it may be a step forward, and research continues.

This is the first reported occurrence of a person being 'cured' of aids in the history of the disease. It still seems a distant prospect for a cure that can be administered to millions pf people worldwide to become available. It might be done by flushing the resting HIV infected cells and replacing them with CCR5, (the cells that HIV latches onto).

CHAPTER THREE

CCR5-delta32 Mutation

A LINK WITH MEDIEVAL TIMES AND 14TH CENTURY BLACK DEATH.

The BLACK DEATH in the year 1346 swept through Northern Europe. Also known as the Bubonic Plague, it went through Northern Europe, killing a large proportion of the population. The disease was found to be unable to affect some of the people, who appeared to have resistance, and ability to stay healthy, despite others dying an unpleasant death. This included those who carried away the dead bodies and buried them. Resistance can be built up by humans and other living creatures. Plants and insects and bacteria can become immune from diseases, the body's defences prevailing.

This is sometimes advantageous and sometimes not. For example medicines which work well can sometimes become ineffective after a while of continuous use. Now it has been found that a gene called CCR5-delta32, which is carried by some people and is thought to be a relic of the great plague in Europe, acts in a similar way. The CCR5-delta32 gives resistance to the white blood cells, and the HIV cannot attach itself to them.

CCR5-delta32 has not long been discovered, and its origins are not certain, but it appears to have saved people in the middle ages from the deadly plague. For the few people who have the CCR5-delta32 gene, and have been in contact with HIV, they appear to have been fortunate. Perhaps I have myself inherited CCR5-delta32, to some extent, because being HIV+ for 30 years or over could explain why I did not die long ago. My reluctance to take AZT in the 1980s is another factor, and friends who took this substance died in the late 1980s and early nineties.

I was considered to be a candidate for a 'trial', to see whether AZT was to be the great breakthrough in the treatment of HIV. This was in 1988 and I was feeling perfectly well at that time.

AZT had been abandoned in the 1960s as a failed cancer drug. It was brought out of 'mothballs' when HIV was discovered, to she what effect it would have as a treatment.

To be asked to take this was a bit scary at the time. I thought that I would have to increase my hospital visits and be checked on by doctors much more often. Not convenient for me I thought. So I said that I would not want to go through with this. The doctor was not happy when I told him that I would rather not have this drug, and that he should give it to someone who was worse than me. The AZT would have caused them to be even more ill, but then that was not known. No other treatment was available, so it was AZT or nothing. I chose the latter and now I am glad that I did.

This was not the end of the AZT story for me. In 1996 I had a feeling of being unwell and my CD4 count was very low. The consultant I was seeing at that time was concerned, and suggested that I take some medications. It had recently been discovered that taking more that one anti-HIV drug at a time would have a much greater effect on combatting the virus than taking one. So that was the start of my drug-taking history, and I was given AZT & 3TC, two different drugs. Combination Therapy was still in its infancy at that time, but now a minimum of three drugs are used.

I felt a lot better in 1997 after stopping the pentamodine gas, and being given septrin (co-trimoxadol) in quite large doses for about a week I began to regain weight and 1998 turned out to be a time when I felt I was 'back to normal' again. It appeared to me that 'the virus' could be fought and overcome, even back in 1997, when treatment was less advanced than today (2014).

CHAPTER FOUR

Conclusion

Today we are told of the dangers of HIV. The media seem to be constantly announcing that the 'deadly disease' is still a grave danger and a cause of death in many countries. Poor living conditions, nutrition and other diseases which are common in 'third world' countries and cause death, but are described as AIDS deaths, is often quoted in the newspapers and on television. This adds to the fear and the dread of the disease, but to the media makes good headlines.

Great amounts of money are spent on research, to produce new drugs and perhaps one day a cure for HIV. After some 30 years no cure has yet been developed, and research continues. Meanwhile we are told of new developments in treatment, such as when to begin treatment, according to our viral load and CD4 count readings, as ascertained by blood tests at the clinic. It is recommended that we take tests for

HIV. This is said that we are then in 'control', but if we test positive this can cause a lot of problems to us. For Example if someone has a problem or illness, and mentions it to the medics, they can just say that it is 'the virus' causing it. Easy to say that when we have been tested HIV+, but to someone who has not been tested and has the same thing, the doctors will have to find another reason, and solution, which is perhaps more difficult.

Retrovirus refers to a virus that develops very slowly. Someone who is infected can live for years without the virus affecting their health. This is why we are told to get a test, so that we can be constantly monitored at the clinics, and have blood tests to ascertain CD4 and Viral Load.

Someone who has tested as HIV negative will be asked to come back for further tests at a later date. Antibodies to HIV do not appear straight away, and can take about three months to appear in the body.

So taking a test can cause problems for the person who decides to do it. If the test is positive it will always be on medical records and the medics will try and persuade us to take pills, whether we want to or not. If the virus is spread from one person to another, the person who infected someone else knowingly could be prosecuted, and go to jail. How it could be proven without doubt would be difficult.

Taking a test therefore is not without its problems, and although we are told that it is what we should do, careful thought seems to be necessary before going ahead. My treatment today consists of three tablets once per day. These are; Prezista (duranavir), Truvada (emtricitabine), and Norvir (ritonavir). These seem to have little or no side effects, unlike one or two others I have tried in the past.

When I took my positive HIV test 28 years ago, I could not see into the future enough to see what life would be like. I felt for certain that I would be clear and HIV-, but I was wrong, and the result came as a shock. After all here I was carrying the 'disease of the century', and in severe trouble, with not much hope for the future. I did not tell anyone about my result, except one or two friends who lived far away. HIV-MUSCLES is the title of the book. At school I was nicknamed Muscles because I was considered to be the 'strongest boy'.

I have smoked in the past, something I did not really like doing, but I became 'hooked' and kept smoking to a minimum, until I gave up completely some 12 years ago. I drink alcohol only in small amounts, and do not take any form of 'recreational' drugs.

HIV-MUSCLES shows that there a way to ward off illness and poor health, and that it is possible for the human body to recover from illness.

I have had tests to try and ascertain why I have not succumbed to the Great Disease of the 20th Century, and made a contribution to medical knowledge, helping others, and showing that there is light at the end of the tunnel.

We are constantly told to 'test' to ascertain whether we have been in contact with HIV. Think carefully and take your time to decide on this. A positive result will change your life, and you will be required to constantly give blood samples and therefore be pricked with needles many times.

So at present I am taking Truvada, Ritonavir, and Duranavir. These are the antiretroviral drugs which l have been prescribed, at my local hospital.

I have supplies of other medicines which are for various other conditions such as diarrhoea, thrush etc. These can occur from time to time.

I am nearly sixty-eight now, and not feeling bad really.

I Hope this information is helpful and will be an interesting account for everyone.

Irvin

www.ingramcontent.com/pod-product-compliance
Lightning Source LLC
Chambersburg PA
CBHW021347310526
45786CB00020B/1980